Chilled Food Association

MICROBIOLOGICAL GUIDANCE FOR PRODUCE SUPPLIERS TO CHILLED FOOD MANUFACTURERS

First Edition
2002

Published by Chilled Food Association Ltd, P O Box 14811, London NW10 9ZR, UK

Typeset in Lucida Sans Unicode 10

Printed in Great Britain by Allstar Services Ltd, 25 Forward Drive, Christchurch Industrial Centre, Harrow, HA3 8NT, UK

ISBN   1 901798 03 8

MICROBIOLOGICAL GUIDANCE FOR PRODUCE SUPPLIERS TO CHILLED FOOD MANUFACTURERS

Contents

Appendices

Tables

Figures

MICROBIOLOGICAL GUIDANCE FOR PRODUCE SUPPLIERS TO CHILLED FOOD MANUFACTURERS

Introduction

Pathogens are endemic in the crop environment, whether or not they are detected. It should be noted that produce cannot ever be sterile and that washing produces at best a 10–100-fold reduction in organisms present.

There have been outbreaks of disease linked to produce, as indicated by the examples of pathogens relevant to produce in Table 1.

To protect the consumer it is necessary to control hazards through the supply chain to the final processor, which can be monitored by sampling for indicator organisms.

The use of HACCP is of increasing importance in primary production and may become a European legal requirement. Suppliers to Chilled Food Association (CFA) members are required to develop HACCP.

This document aims to assist in the development of HACCP by addressing Critical Control Points and by providing clear guidance to all growers of produce on the main microbial food safety hazards and their controls, particularly in relation to produce that is to be minimally processed and eaten without being cooked.

This guidance is based on current best knowledge, but since this is a relatively new area of scientific study the guidance will be reviewed as further information arises.

By implementing the recommendations in this guidance you will help to minimise the risks of a food poisoning outbreaks associated with fresh produce. This will protect both the consumer and your business.

All UK growers supplying CFA members are required to be members of 'Assured Produce'. Overseas growers should be members of a recognised, independently audited local assurance scheme. All growers should be working towards the EUREP GAP scheme independently or through development and accreditation of their current scheme.

CFA Members use suppliers who demonstrate that they supply a quality product and follow Good Agricultural Practice (GAP).

1. Definitions

Aerobic Colony Count

A measure of the total number of aerobic bacteria present in a sample. ACC has replaced the previous name 'aerobic plate count' or 'Total Viable Count' or 'Total Colony Count'.

Bacteria

Single-celled microorganisms that lack a fully defined nucleus and contain no chlorophyll. Bacteria of the coliform group are considered the primary indicators of faecal contamination and are often used to assess water quality.

CFU (Colony Forming Unit)

Microbial cells forming a single colony on an agar plate.

Clean

Remove soil and physical matter from surfaces by physical and/or chemical means.

Cleaning Schedule

Documentation of cleaning and decontamination methods, frequencies and appropriate monitoring procedures for plant, equipment and the environment.

Deep Clean

A process of intensive and rigorous cleaning that may involve disassembly of the item being cleaned.

Coliforms

Coliform bacteria are members of the family *Enterobacteriaceae*. They can be represented by four groups: *Citrobacter, Enterobacter, Escherichia* and *Klebsiella*.

Composting

A managed biological process of oxidation of solid organic material that includes a thermal phase.

Contamination

The introduction or occurrence of a contaminant in a food product, ingredient or environment.

Contaminant

Physical matter, microorganisms, toxins or chemicals that may compromise food safety or quality.

Critical Control Point (CCP)

A step at which control can be applied and is essential to prevent or eliminate a food safety hazard or reduce it to an acceptable level.

Decontamination

Removal or reduction of contaminant(s) to an acceptable level for safety or quality.

Disinfection

Microbiological decontamination.

EHEC (Enterohaemorrhagic *E. coli*

EHEC are a subset of VTEC that may be associated with bloody diarrhoea.

Enterobacteriaceae

A large group of heat sensitive, rod-shaped bacteria found in the environment and faeces, and which include coliforms. The most significant *Enterobacteriaceae* in terms of human foodborne disease are *Salmonella, Shigella, Escherichia*, and *Yersinia*

Escherichia coli (E. coli)

A species of faecal coliform bacteria. *E. coli* is part of the normal intestinal flora in humans and animals and is, therefore, a direct indicator of faecal contamination including in water. There are many strains of *E. coli*, one of which is the O157 strain, which can cause serious infection and even death.

Faecal Pathogens

Pathogens originating in the gastrointestinal tract of warm-blooded animals such as humans and animals.

Farm Yard Manure (FYM)

Excrement (faeces and urine) of farm animals often mixed with straw from bedding.

Gastroenteritis

An infection or irritation of the stomach and intestines. May be caused by bacteria or parasites. Symptoms may include diarrhoea, nausea, vomiting, and abdominal cramping.

Good Agricultural Practice (GAP)

The adoption of management practices that minimise the risks of water, air and soil pollution, ensure the highest possible standards of food safety and allow economic agriculture to continue.

Good Hygienic Practice

Activities/operations that are conducted such that the microbiological integrity of the product is not compromised.

Hazard

A biological, chemical or physical agent in, or condition of, food with the potential to cause an adverse health effect.

Hazard Analysis Critical Control Points (HACCP)

A system that identifies specific hazard(s) and preventative measures for their control. See Annex B of CFA's Guidelines for Good Hygienic Practice in the Manufacture of Chilled Foods.

HACCP Plan

A formal document comprising key information from the HACCP study including details of all that is critical to food safety management. The Plan consists of two essential components – the process flow diagram and HACCP control chart, along with any other necessary documentation, which supports the planned management of food safety hazards.

Indicator Organism

An organism used to indicate the potential presence of other (usually pathogenic) organisms. Indicator organisms are usually associated with the other organisms, but are usually more easily sampled and measured.

Microbiological criteria

Define the acceptability of a product or a food lot, based on the absence or presence, or number of microorganisms including parasites, and/or quantity of their toxins/metabolites, per unit(s) of mass, volume, area or lot.

Microbiological risk

The potential for food to contain bacteria, viruses, yeasts, moulds and algae, parasitic protozoa and helminths, and their toxins or metabolites.

Microorganisms

Bacteria, viruses, yeasts, moulds and parasites.

Parasite

An animal or plant living in or on an organism of another species (its host), obtaining from it part or all of its organic nutriment, and commonly exhibiting some degree of adaptive structural modification. The host never benefits from this presence.

Pathogen

An agent capable of causing disease, especially microorganisms, but also parasites.

Confirmed Pathogen

An isolate whose identity has been confirmed as a pathogen.

Presumptive Pathogen

An isolate showing the characteristics of a pathogen from further tests, but not yet confirmed.

Suspected Pathogen

An isolate on a primary plating medium that is highly likely to be confirmed as a target pathogen, e.g. on the basis of colony morphology.

Primary Preparation

Cleaning and trimming of raw materials.

Primary Washing

Removal of excess soil and debris.

Protozoa

Single celled animals, some of which can cause human disease.

Ready to Eat (RTE)

A product, component or ingredient that can reasonably be expected to be eaten without any further microbial reduction process e.g. thermal treatment.

Risk

A function of the probability of an adverse health effect and the severity of that effect, consequential to a hazard(s) in food.

Risk Analysis

A process consisting of three components: risk assessment, risk management and risk communication.

Risk Assessment

A scientifically based process consisting of the following steps:

(i)   Hazard identification
(ii)   Hazard characterisation
(iii)   Exposure assessment
(iv)   Risk characterisation

Risk Assessment Policy

Documented guidelines for scientific judgment and policy choices to be applied at appropriate decision points during the risk assessment.

Risk Characterisation

The process of determining the qualitative and/or quantitative estimation, including attendant uncertainties, of the probability of occurrence and severity of known or potential adverse health effects in a given population based on hazard identification, hazard characterization and exposure assessment.

Risk Communication

The interactive exchange of information and opinions throughout the risk analysis process concerning risk, risk related factors and risk perception among risk assessors, risk managers, consumers, industry, the academic community and other interested parties, including the explanation of risk assessment findings and the basis of risk management decisions.

Risk Management

The process, distinct from risk assessment, of weighing policy alternatives, in consultation with all interested parties, considering risk assessment and other factors relevant for the health protection of consumers and for the promotion of fair trade practices, and if needed selecting appropriate prevention and control options.

Sample

A part of a lot or batch, being representative of that lot or batch.

Sampling Plan

A sampling plan includes the sampling procedure and the decision criteria to be applied to a lot, based on examination of a prescribed number of sample units and subsequent analytical units of a stated size by defined methods. A well-designed sampling plan defines the probability of detecting microorganisms in a lot, but it should be borne in mind that no sampling plan can ensure the absence of a particular organism.

Sewage Sludge

Residues obtained from residual water treatment plants and from treatment applied to urban and industrial wastes.

Secondary Preparation

Size reduction of raw materials following primary preparation.

Spoilage Organism

An organism that causes food to become organoleptically unacceptable due either to the growth of the organisms itself or the effect of its growth on the integrity of the foodstuff.

Total coliform bacteria

A particular group of bacteria, found in the faeces of warm-blooded animals that are used as indicators of possible sewage pollution. Since many common soil bacteria are also coliforms, but do not indicate faecal contamination, a total coliform test will show the presence of all coliforms including many common soil bacteria which do not indicate faecal contamination. Therefore this test should not be interpreted as showing only coliforms derived from faeces.

Virus

An infectious agent smaller than a bacterium, which needs a host to reproduce.

VTEC (Verocytotoxigenic *E. coli*)

VTEC are a group of highly infective and virulent *E. coli,* producing potent toxins. *E. coli* O157 is the most prevalent VTEC in the UK. However not all *E coli* O157 strains are VTEC. VTEC cause a wide range of diseases ranging from simple diarrhoea and HUS (Haemolytic Uraemic Syndrome), which can lead to permanent loss of kidney function.

Water

Clean water

Water that does not compromise food safety in the circumstances of its use.

Ground Water

Water that has percolated through the soil from the surface and is available in porous rock beneath the surface.

Potable water

Water that is of drinking water standard as defined in the legislation European Communities (Quality of Water Intended for Human Consumption) Regulations 1998.

Surface Water

Rivers, lakes, ponds, reservoirs, uncovered storage tanks etc where the water source is open to the environment.

2.   Hazard Organisms of Concern & Their Origin

Pathogenic organisms are widespread in the crop environment and must be controlled.

An example of the common origins of foodborne pathogens, in this case *E. coli* O157, is shown in Figure 1 below.

Animal waste, human waste and water are important vehicles for transmission of pathogens to crops and therefore require careful control.

Figure 1: Origin of *E. coli* O157

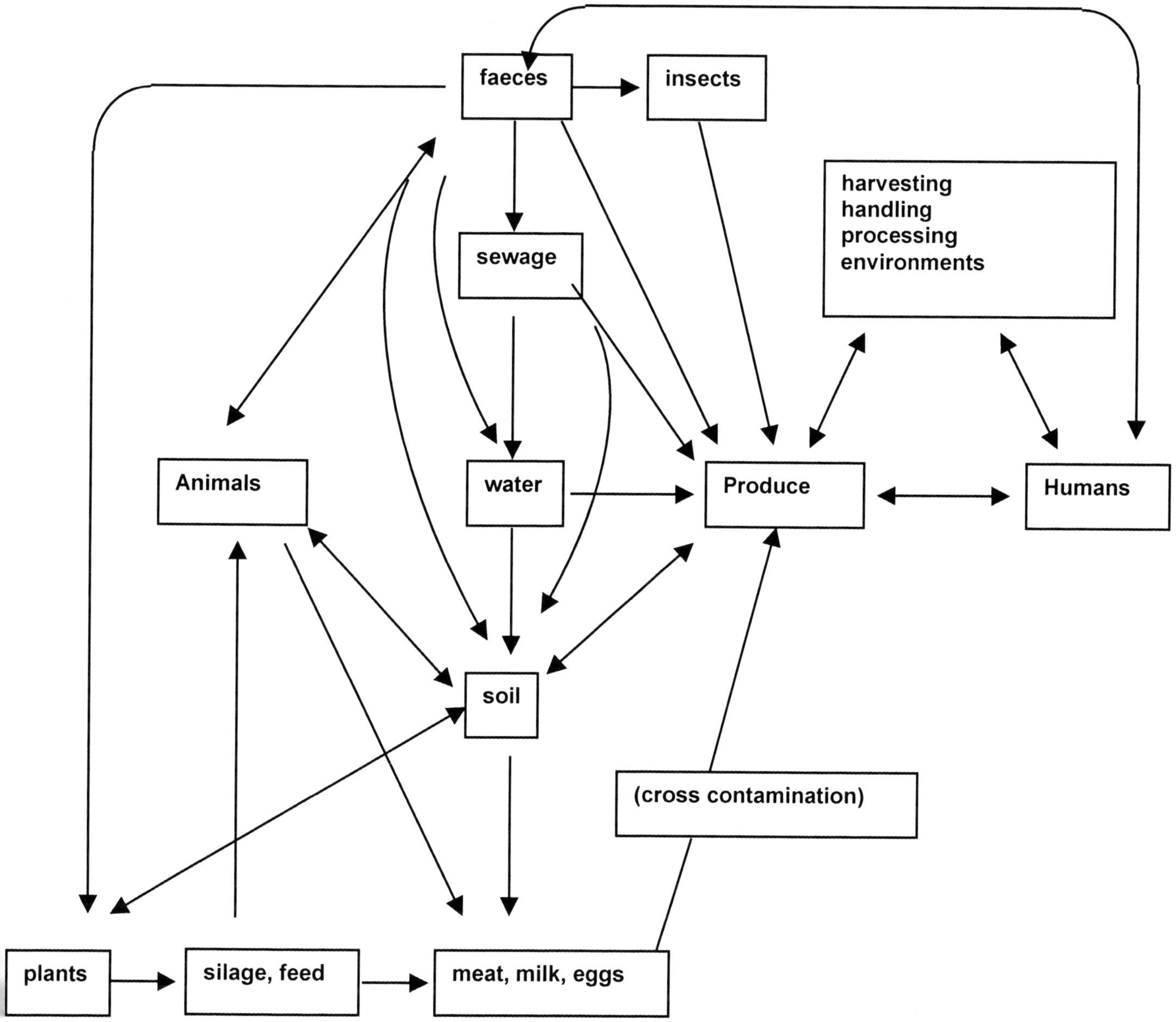

Table 1: Key Groups of Pathogens Relevant to Produce, with Examples

Pathogen Group	Examples	Disease
Viruses	*Norwalk virus*	Acute gastroenteritis
	Hepatitis A virus	Infectious hepatitis
	Rotavirus	Acute gastroenteritis
Bacteria	*Salmonella sp*	Salmonellosis (gastroenteritis)
	Campylobacter jejuni	Campylobacteriosis (gastroenteritis)
	EHEC (Enterohaemorrhagic E coli)	A variety of gastroenteric diseases
	Shigella sp	Bacillary dysentery
	S typhi sp	Typhoid fever
	V cholerae	Cholera
Protozoa	*Giardia lamblia*	Giardiasis (gastroenteritis)
	Cryptosporidium sp	Cryptosporidiosis (gastroenteritis)

Reference: Derived from PHLS, 2000

3.   HACCP

The HACCP (Hazard Analysis Critical Control Point) system is used throughout the food industry to identify hazards and their controls, focusing on prevention rather than relying mainly on end product testing.

The use of HACCP is of increasing importance in primary production and may become a European legal requirement. However, suppliers to Chilled Food Association members are required to develop HACCP.

Briefly, HACCP is applied by taking a number of simple steps:-

- Reviewing the process (in this case growing and harvesting) from start to finish
- Deciding where hazards could occur
- Putting in controls to eliminate hazards or reduce them to acceptable levels
- Monitoring controls
- Documenting all the above and keeping records
- Ensuring that the system continues to work effectively

The purpose of the HACCP system is to focus control at Critical Control Points (CCPs). CCPs can be determined using a decision tree (Figure 2).

Figure 2: Example of Decision Tree to Identify Critical Control Points

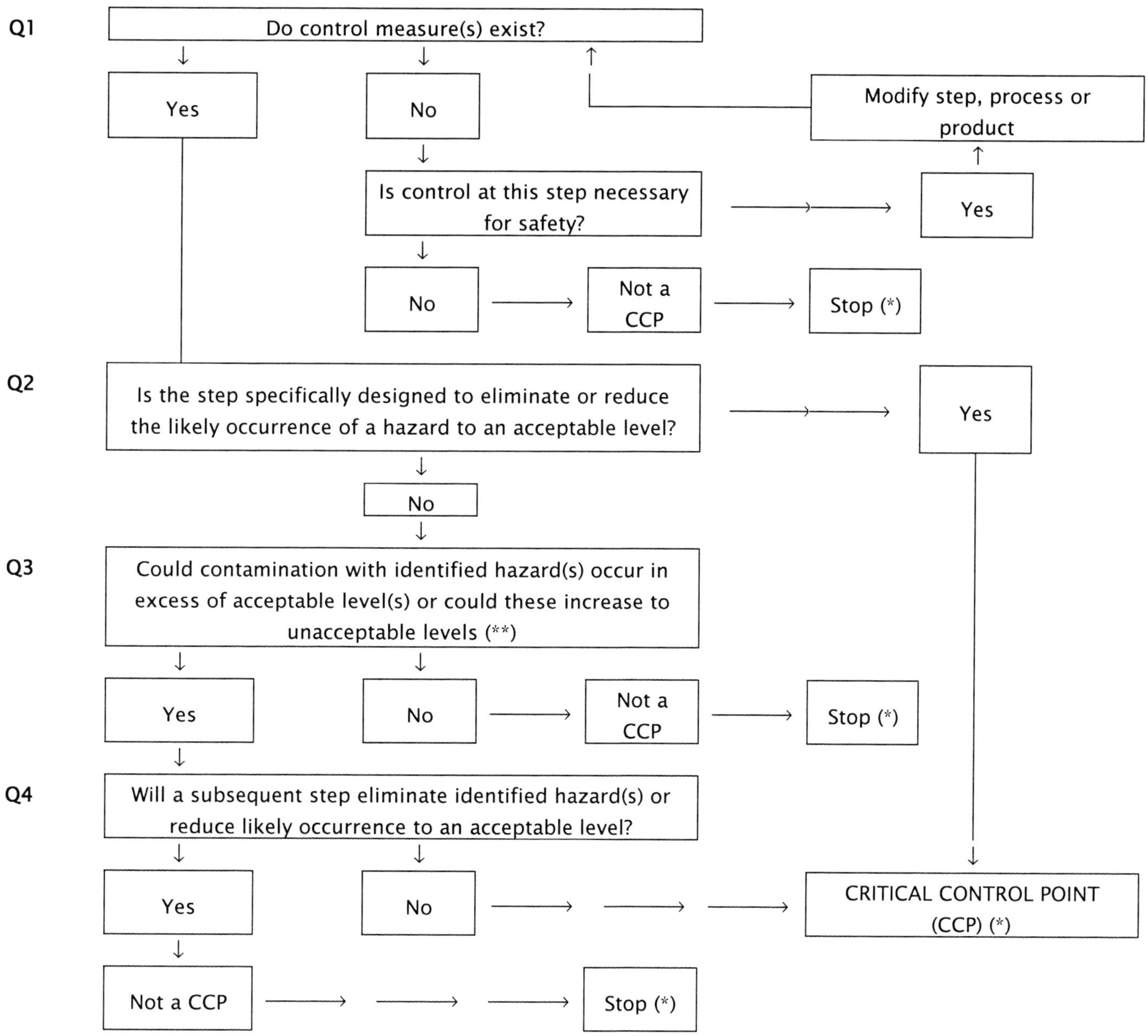

(*)   Proceed to the next identified hazard in the process

(**) Acceptable and unacceptable levels need to be defined within the overall objectives in identifying the CCPs of the HACCP plan.

Source: CODEX Alimentarius Commission, General Principles of Food Hygiene.

The successful application of HACCP requires the full commitment and involvement of the management and the workforce.   The HACCP team should be multidisciplinary.

Hazard analysis should be based on an assessment of risk, with the likeliness of a food hazard occurring and the severity of its effects forming part of this process.

The control of hazards that may subsequently affect the severity and nature of microbiological contamination of the produce must be encompassed within the HACCP plan.

It is advisable to document the identified hazards and their controls.

The HACCP plan should be drawn up by a person who knows the operation, be verified and reviewed regularly by management and whenever there is a change of product, or process (e.g. change of irrigation water source) or a significant change of personnel.

Records of problems encountered and corrective action taken should be in place, written up and be available for inspection.

Hazard analysis can form the basis of a good quality system.

Useful Information Sources

Training courses can be found listed on the CFA website's events page: www.chilledfood.org/events.htm

Assured Crop Production – HACCP Case Studies for Farmers and Growers
Supplements CCFRA Guideline No. 10 (1999)

'HACCP: A Practical Guide'
CCFRA Technical Manual No. 38 2nd Edition (1997)

'HACCP: a practical approach'
Mortimore and Wallace, Chapman & Hall, (1994), ISBN 0 412 57020 3

HACCP in Agriculture and Horticulture (Second Edition)
CCFRA Guideline No. 10 (2000)

'Making the Most of HACCP: Learning from others' experience'
Eds Mayes and Mortimore, Woodhead Publishing, (2001), ISBN 1 85573 504 0

'The Application of HACCP to Horticulture, with Emphasis on Microbial Safety of Produce'
Jose Spring, MSc Thesis, University of Reading, 1998.

HACCP Documentation Software (Version 3.0)
CCFRA

4. Traceability

Growers should develop procedures to track product from the field or plot to the recipient in as much detail as possible, and, as a minimum, provide documentation to indicate the source of a product and a mechanism for marking or identifying the product that can track the product from the farm to the consumer.

It is essential with the HACCP system to be able to trace batches of raw materials or products in the event of a failure at a CCP.

An effective traceability system must link a lot or batch with its growing site and any treatment it has received throughout its growth or postharvest.

An effective traceability system will allow rapid access to information on products and can limit the potential scope of a problem associated with a raw material. It can be therefore used to help identify where the source of the problem might be.

This documentation must include information on:-

- Lot number
- Date of harvest
- Identity of the farm (plot or field), producer and country of origin
- The chain of ownership of the material from the grower to recipient
- Agricultural inputs (e.g. manure/fertiliser, irrigation and pesticides), dates of application and input lot numbers

Procedures should be developed to enable the complete and rapid recall of any implicated produce and provide detailed information to assist in the identification and investigation of any contaminated material.

These can include out of hours contact details and sources of assistance, which must be kept up to date.

Key points:-

- The emergency procedure must be documented and available to all relevant staff
- The procedure must be capable of being put into operation at short notice at any time
- Incidents must be fully recorded and reviewed
- Procedures should be tested regularly

Full traceability, linking a lot/batch with the field and the treatment it has received is a legislative requirement within the Food Safety Act 1990 and the EC general principles of food law Regulation (EC, 2002).

5. Hazards and their Control in Growing

5.1 Seed

Seed can be contaminated before it is germinated. This is of particular importance in the production of sprouted products.

Key points:

- Manure should only be applied to land when it has undergone effective treatments to eliminate the risks of foodborne pathogens (see Table 3).
- Animals must not be allowed to graze fields where seeds are grown for a minimum of six months prior to drilling (see Table 5).
- Exposure of seeds to mist and high humidity should be avoided

It is particularly important to prevent microbial contamination during the production of seeds because of the potential for pathogens to grow during the sprouting process.

The following additional points should therefore be addressed in relation to the production of seeds for sprouting:

- Diseased or damaged seeds should not be despatched for sprout production
- Seeds for sprout production must be segregated from those to be used as animal feed
- Seeds should be tested for microbial pathogens using an appropriate sampling plan

The source, microbiological quality and transportation of the seed should also be investigated and assessed.

For further information see 'Hygienic manufacture, distribution and retail sale of sprouted seeds', Technical Manual 25, CCFRA, Chipping Campden, UK, GL55 6LD.

5.2 Field

The history, (preferably the last 5 years), of the use of the field should be known, including those of adjoining sites. These should be evaluated to identify potential microbial, chemical and physical hazards that could arise from agricultural inputs, for example.

This should include consideration of use for:-

- Crop production (type)
- Animal production/grazing and application of animal manures/sewage sludge
- Hazardous waste site, e.g. industrial wastes, abattoir waste, manure piles
- Sewage treatment site
- Mining extraction site
- History of flooding

Many produce crops are grown in proximity to the soil. For most foodborne pathogens, animal or human faeces are the commonest source of contamination, thus due consideration should be given to possible faecal contamination of the field, and measures taken to avoid its occurrence.

The access of farm and wild animals to the site and to water sources used in primary production are potential routes of faecal contamination of the soil and water. The risk of this contaminating crops must be evaluated.

Animals must not be allowed to graze fields where food crops are grown, including seeds.

The potential for contaminating crops from leaking or overflowing manure storage sites, flooding and by slurry spraying must be evaluated. There must also be awareness of the treatments applied to neighbouring fields, as slurry spray can be carried by a moderate wind for up to one kilometre.

5.3   Farmyard Manure, Compost and Faecal Material (Sewage Sludge)

There are many types of fertiliser, some of which are not pathogen risks. However, farmyard manure and sewage sludge are the most common of those presenting risks.

5.3.1   Farmyard Manure

Farmyard manure (FYM) is a valuable source of plant nutrients and organic matter, which can assist in maintaining soil fertility. However, FYM in its raw state also contains a high proportion of faecal material and may contain foodborne pathogens. The numbers present depend upon the source of the manure (see Table 2), health of the livestock and management practices between production and land spreading.

Table 2: Examples of Relative Risks of Various Manure Sources

Manure Source	Relative Risk
Cattle	Highest
Pig	
	↓
Sheep	
Chicken	Lowest

Manure heaps should be composted for at least three months prior to use of the material (see Table 3).

FYM should be composted before being applied to the soil by ploughing in so that the risk of run-off into a water source is avoided.

Growers purchasing manure should take account of the source and the treatment that it may have undergone before use.

Acceptable treatments of FYM for use in agriculture are set out in Table 3.

Table 3: Acceptable Treatments of Farmyard Manure/Slurry

Treatment	Process
Active (slurries) • Lime treatment	 • pH>12 for at least 12 hours
Batch (solid and slurries)	At least 6 months storage or 'active' treatment
Composting (solid)	Turned at least twice, >55°C throughout for at least 3 days and stored for at least 3 months

The application of FYM should be in time to ensure the breakdown of organic matter to facilitate drilling/planting.

Since the treatment of manure is not an exact science and there is a chance that some pathogens may survive, the interval between manure application and produce harvest should be maximised to minimise risks of contaminating produce.

Manures and slurries must not be applied directly to growing salad and fruit crops or within a 50-metre radius of a water source.

Slurry must not be sprayed within 1 km upwind of or on fields adjacent to crops since microorganisms can be carried in aerosols.

Raw FYM cannot be used on a crop rotation a minimum of 12 months before drilling/planting a horticultural crop. Refer to Table 5 regarding livestock intervals.

Requirements relating to raw FYM intervals will be reviewed once FSA-funded research currently in progress is completed.

5.3.2 Sewage Sludge

The use of untreated (raw) sludge use on agricultural land is not permitted.

Although the use of treated sewage sludge is acceptable in the ADAS Safe Sludge Matrix (see Table 4 below), the use of sewage sludge (treated or not) on salad crops is not good practice.

Limitations on the use of digested sludge are given in Table 4.

Table 4: The Safe Application of Sewage Sludge to Agricultural Land: The ADAS Matrix

Crop	Untreated Sludge	Digested Sludge	Enhanced Treated Sludges
Fruit	No	No	Yes 10 month harvest interval applies
Salad	No	30 month harvest interval	Yes 10 month harvest interval applies
Vegetables	No	12 month harvest interval	Yes 10 month harvest interval applies
Horticulture	No	No	Yes 10 month harvest interval applies
Combinable & Animal Feed Crops	No	Yes	Yes
Grass and forage		3 week no grazing and harvest interval applies:	3 week no grazing and harvest interval applies:
• Grazed	No	No (deep injected or ploughed down only)	Yes
• Harvested	No	Yes (no grazing in season of application)	Yes

Enhanced treated sludges are defined as being free from *Salmonella* and will have been treated so as to ensure that 99.9999% of pathogens have been destroyed (6 log reduction).

Your local sewerage operator will be able to provide further details of the treatment method used as this will affect where and when sludge can be applied. There is a 48-month exclusion period following contamination of land with untreated sewage sludge.

The latest version of the Safe Sludge Matrix can be found at www.adas.co.uk/matrix.

For technical queries relating to the interpretation and application of the matrix contact ADAS (address given in section 11).

5.3.3 Animals and Birds

Animal and bird contact with crops and land is a potential source of contamination. Measures to prevent domesticated and farm animals and livestock from accessing crop fields must be taken. Good field margin management shall be employed. Steps should be taken to discourage animal activity within the crop, such as the removal of crop debris.

Table 5: Livestock Intervals

Livestock	Drilling/Planting Interval
Cattle	12 months
Other livestock	6 months

5.3.4 Water

Water is used in numerous field and glasshouse operations including:-

- Irrigation (in glasshouse and field)
- Makeup and application of fertilisers
- Crop protection sprays
- Cooling systems

Water is a potential source of foodborne pathogens; therefore practices or processes involving water should be evaluated in terms of potential sources and routes of contamination, e.g. animal and human waste.

Measures should be put in place to limit the possibility for waterborne contamination and to ensure that water quality is appropriate for its intended use.

5.3.4.1 Source and Storage

In general, the risk of contamination is greatest for surface water supplies, less for ground water supplies, and significantly less for municipal water supplies.

Table 6: Examples of Relative Risks of Various Water Sources

Water Source	Relative Risk
Surface	Highest
Ground	↓
Municipal (Potable)	Lowest

Sources of water used for whatever purpose should be identified, and its microbial and chemical quality assessed together with suitability for intended use and measures to prevent or minimise contamination (e.g. from livestock, other animals, run-off from heavy rainfall and excess irrigation).

Water can be stored in closed, underground or capped well systems, which are not usually subject to the risk of surface contamination.

5.3.4.2 Quality

It should be noted that testing only reflects water quality at the time of sampling.

Growers should arrange for periodic testing of water for microbial contamination, the frequency based on risk assessment.

Testing for total *E. coli* is recommended.

Additional microorganisms, such as pathogens of major concern (Salmonella, faecal Streptococci, protozoa etc), may be tested for if there is a potential or suspected hazard.

5.3.4.3 Application

The time gap between irrigation and crop harvesting should be maximised.

The potential for contaminated water to come into contact with the edible portion of the product should be minimised by good practice, such as drip, furrow or underground irrigation.

Produce with a relatively large surface area and with physical characteristics such as leaves and rough surfaces, presents a greater risk of trapping water, accentuating water quality effects.

Water quality may need to be greater for overhead spray irrigation than for drip irrigation.

Table 7: Examples of Relative Risks – Irrigation Method

Irrigation Method	Relative Risk
Overhead spray	Highest
Drip	
Furrow	↓
Underground	Lowest

5.3.4.4 Crop Type

The risk of pathogens being transferred to crops by irrigation water varies depending on the crop type and its final usage. For example, open growing baby leaf crops that are to be eaten raw carry the highest risk (see Table 8).

Table 8: Examples of Relative Risks – Crop Types, Uses

Crop Type	Crop End Use	Relative Risk
Baby Leaf	Raw, RTE	Highest
Leaf	Raw, RTE	
Stem	Raw, RTE	
Root Vegetable	Raw, RTE	↓
Leaf, Stem, Root vegetable	To be cooked	
Combinable	Heat processed	Lowest

The aim is to minimise such inherent risks by usage of low risk agricultural practices, such as low risk irrigation methods.

5.3.4.5 Hygiene

Equipment used for the application and storage of water must be regularly inspected for cleanliness and cleaned as appropriate.

5.4 Useful Information Sources

'A Study on Farm Manure Applications to Agricultural Land and an Assessment of the Risks of Pathogen Transfer into the Food Chain'
A report to: The Ministry of Agriculture Fisheries and Food, ADAS, January 2000
Project Number: FS2526

'Briefing Paper: Manure Management in Organic Farming. Campaigning for organic food and farming and sustainable forestry'
Soil Association, 2000

Code of Practice for Agricultural Use of Sewage Sludge
DEFRA publications sales unit, Tel: +44 (0) 1709 891318

Codes of Good Agricultural Practice for the Protection of Water, Air and Soil
DEFRA publications Tel: +44 (0) 645 556 000

'Common Zoonoses in Agriculture'
Agriculture Information Sheet No. 2 (rev), HSE, P O Box 1999, Sudbury, CO10 6FS.

'Design and Construction Guidelines for Farm Waste Storage'
Scottish Agricultural College, Auchinruive, Ayr, Scotland, KA6 5HW. ISBN 1 85482 481 3

'Guidelines for the Safe Use of Wastewater and Excreta in Agriculture and Aquaculture. Measures for Public Health Protection'
Mara & Cairncross, World Health Organisation, 1989, ISBN 92 4 154248 9

Prevention of Environmental Pollution from Agricultural Activity
Scottish Office, Environment & Fisheries Dept, 1997. Tel: 0131 244 0312

Regulation (EC) 178/2002 Laying Down the General Principles and Requirements of Food Law, Establishing the European Food Safety Authority and Laying Down Procedures in Matters of Food Safety, (2002).
Official Journal of the European Communities, L 31, pp1–24, 1 February 2002.

'The Safe Sludge Matrix – Guidelines for the Application of Sewage Sludge to Agricultural Land' www.adas.co.uk/matrix, ADAS, 2001.

'Water for Irrigation'
Ref 011 241 5199, MAFF. DEFRA publications Tel: +44 (0) 645 556 000

6.   Harvesting & Handling

People harvesting crops are food handlers and should therefore meet the same health, training and good practice requirements as those elsewhere in the food chain.

As soon as a crop is harvested, trimmed and packed it becomes a food and is subject to the Food Safety (General Food Hygiene) Regulations 1995 and Food Safety Act 1990. However, as RTE produce does not undergo a process that totally eliminates pathogens, the principles of good food safety management should be applied to the entire supply chain from the seed to the final product.

6.1   People

Pre-employment screening of food handlers should comprise satisfactory completion of a medical questionnaire (see Appendix 2) and satisfactory completion of food safety awareness assessment (Appendix 3).

All food handlers must be trained in food hygiene and managers are expected to attend a formal hygiene training course.

Records of all staff training must be kept for inspection

Hands must be washed:

Before...	After...
Handling protective clothing	Handling waste
Putting on gloves	Using the toilet
Entering food handling areas	Blowing your nose
	Carrying out cleaning duties

Cuts and blemishes must be covered with a blue waterproof plaster.

Toilet facilities must be

- Provided for field staff and be accessible at any time to ensure their use
- Located in close proximity to the fields
- Of appropriate design to ensure hygienic removal of wastes and avoid contamination of growing sites, crops and agricultural inputs
- Fitted with adequate means of hygienically washing, sanitising and drying hands. Single use disposable paper towels are the preferred method of drying hands after washing. Alcohol sanitiser may be used.
- Maintained under sanitary conditions and good repair at all times
- Located to minimise the potential for contamination of crops in the event of a leakage or spill (e.g. downhill from fields)

There should be no smoking, spitting, chewing gum or eating, sneezing or coughing over unprotected produce.

Eating and drinking should be done away from the crop, preferably in a designated area, e.g. a headland.

6.2 Equipment

Equipment and containers coming into contact with fresh produce and crops should be designed and constructed to facilitate adequate cleaning, disinfection and maintenance.

Containers for waste and inedible or dangerous substances should be specifically identifiable, suitably constructed and, where appropriate, made of impervious material. They must not be used for carrying harvested product or seeds.

Mobile field harvesting rigs must be kept clean and tidy and in good working order at all times. In particular:-

- Control of physical, microbiological and chemical contamination must be addressed through hazard analysis.
- A realistic and rigidly applied cleaning schedule with detailed procedures must be implemented and its efficacy tested on a regular basis.
- Equipment such as conveyors and pallets should be free from obvious contaminants (mud, diesel, grease, oil, waste produce and debris etc).
- All knives should be cleaned and stored appropriately when not in use.
- All knives must be accounted for and checked for damage after harvesting, and appropriate action taken to deal with any defects.
- Packaging must be kept clean, away from soil contamination

6.3 Weather Conditions

The weather conditions during growing and at the point of harvest, can affect the visual/microbiological quality of the final product. It is good practice to notify the Customer of adverse conditions to allow the opportunity for process optimisation and increased microbiological/visual monitoring.

6.4 Primary Preparation (Washing)

Postharvest washing treatments may be carried out, typically to remove soil from root vegetables. HACCP should be conducted on this process and particular attention given to controlling and monitoring the quality of wash water. A monitoring and testing regime should be in place to demonstrate control, identifying trends and allow reporting of the presence of pathogens. Excess moisture may provide conditions conducive to microbial growth, loss of quality and reduction of shelf life.

6.5 Storage

Effective measures must be taken to prevent cross-contamination of fresh produce from agricultural inputs or personnel who come directly or indirectly into contact with fresh produce.

Storage facilities should be designed and constructed in such a way as to minimise damage to fresh produce and to avoid access by pests and to reduce the opportunity for potential contamination from physical objects such as glass, wood, metal etc.

Fresh produce unfit for human consumption should be segregated and clearly identified.

No harvested fresh produce for human consumption must be stored outdoors without cover.

6.6 Useful Information Sources

'Food Hygiene – An Industry Guide'
Fresh Produce Consortium.

'Guide to Minimize Microbial Food Safety Hazards for Fresh Fruits and Vegetables'
U.S. Department of Health and Human Services/Food and Drug Administration/Center for Food Safety and Applied Nutrition (CFSAN), 1999

'Hygiene in Fresh Produce Handling '
CCFRA Seminar Proceedings (1998)

'The control of microbial hazards: A produce industry guide'
Fresh Produce Consortium, 1998.

7. Transport and Temperature Control

Contamination of produce may occur due to improper practices during loading, unloading and transportation operations. Appropriate temperature control will limit the potential for growth of any contaminating microorganisms, maintaining quality over shelf life. However, certain produce items such as tropical/exotic fruits are sensitive to chill temperatures.

7.1 Cooling

The method of cooling must be appropriate to the product type.

Condensate and defrost water from evaporator type cooling systems (e.g. vacuum cooling, cold rooms) must not drip onto fresh produce.

An appropriate biocide should be used in condenser trays to prevent contamination build up.

Water and ice used in cooling is a potential source of microbial contamination.

- Growers should only use potable water for cooling and for making ice
- The water should be tested periodically for contaminants (see section 5 (e) (ii))

Where water is used as an integral part of a cooling system it should originate from a potable source. Due regard should be paid to the risk of contamination of recirculated water in cooling systems.

Consideration should also be given to the Health and Safety risk from *Legionella* due to the creation of aerosols.

Cooling to <10°C should be done as soon as possible after harvesting to minimise the risk of pathogen growth and consideration made of the prevailing time temperature conditions regarding microbial risk should be given.

Equipment such as hydro-coolers and containers holding produce during cooling should be clean and sanitary.

Air cooling systems should be designed and maintained to avoid contaminating fresh produce. They must be clean and the cool air free from microbiological contaminants.

7.2   Storage and Transport

7.2.1   Chill chain

The chill chain should operate at a target maximum of 5°C but the precise temperature chosen will be dependent on the type of produce in question owing to the potential for chill injury.

The temperature of cold storage should be controlled and monitored.

7.2.2   Cleanliness of vehicles and their previous use

Vehicles must be keep clean to reduce the risk of microbial contamination or cross-contamination of fresh produce. The use of produce specific vehicles is strongly recommended.

Vehicles previously used for the transportation of waste or animal materials and products should not be used for the transportation of fresh produce without through cleaning and disinfection beforehand. Consideration should also be given to whether vehicles have been used for meat or meat products, fish, shellfish, nuts and other recognised allergens in order to manage the risk of cross contamination.

Cleaning to remove residual materials, odours and other forms of contamination must be sufficiently thorough such that there is no risk to the produce. Disinfectants must be rinsed off to ensure that produce is not tainted.

Produce must not be cross contaminated.

Care must be taken to minimise the damage caused to produce when loading onto vehicles.

8.   **Packhouses/Post Harvest Handling**

Poor sanitation in the packhouse environment can significantly increase the risk of contaminating fresh produce and water.

Pathogenic microorganisms may be found on any food contact surfaces including packaging as well as on packhouse floors, walls, ceilings and drains.

Checks made at start up and after deep cleaning must be recorded, to include visual inspection of contact surfaces.

Damaged or muddy containers should be repaired, cleaned or discarded in order to reduce possible microbial contamination of fresh produce.

All personnel including produce inspectors, buyers and other visitors must thoroughly wash their hands before handling produce.

9. Sampling, Test Methods, Targets and Tolerances, Interpretation of Results

9.1 Sampling

Raw material product testing cannot be used as a control measure – hazard control in the field is key. Microbiological testing may be of some value in verifying controls in the field and in handling, and to provide trend data.

Sampling and testing of irrigation water can be used to give an indication of microbiological quality, which must be managed to minimise its impact on the safety of the crop.

Growers are encouraged to use a suitable screening protocol using recognised standard methods for harvested produce to ascertain the nature and level of microbiological contamination. This produces a database of levels and enables appropriate reaction to high or positive results.

Samples shall be taken in such a way as to avoid their contamination (see Appendix 1).

Reputable laboratories accredited to a national or international standard and having expertise in testing for and finding organisms of concern in produce or water (as applicable) must be used for analytical work. However, the use of kits for screening using indicator organisms is acceptable when suspect results are then followed up using standard laboratory methods.

9.2 Test Methods

Methods used must be validated for the sample type in question. Due to the high levels of microorganisms naturally present in produce, methods have to be highly selective. Microorganisms similar to those pathogens of concern may cause false positive results. Expert advice should be sought for recommended methods and interpretation of validation data for methods. Rapid methods, especially for pathogens, should be avoided unless full validation for the sample type has been satisfactorily carried out.

9.3 Targets and Tolerances

9.3.1 Water

There are no standards set for the microbiological quality of irrigation water. Microbiological levels can be expected to be much higher than those stated for potable water. Levels will be in relation to the source, which should be risk assessed (Table 5).

World Health Organisation standards for potable water are absence of coliforms and *E. coli* in 100ml. ACC can be carried out as an indicator of quality trends.

There are not set standards for ACC, trend data should be kept and a significant rise in levels should be investigated.

9.3.2 Foodstuffs

The PHLS Guidelines for the microbiological quality of some ready-to-eat foods sampled at the point of sale (PHLS, 2000) are useful for determining the significance of the presence of pathogens in foods at any point of sale of a RTE product. However, since these are only guidelines, they are not prescriptive and have no legal standing in their own right.

Interpretation of the guidelines should be based on knowledge of the product components and the production process.

9.3.2.1 Pathogens

Produce should be free from *Salmonella* spp, *Campylobacter*, *E. coli* O157 and other Verocytotoxin producing *E. coli* (VTEC), Shigella spp and *Vibrio cholerae* in (25 gramme samples). THE CONFIRMATION OF THE PRESENCE OF ANY OF THESE ORGANISMS MUST BE ACTED UPON IMMEDIATELY.

9.3.2.1.1 *Listeria monocytogenes*

Listeria monocytogenes is widely distributed in the environment and is able to multiply slowly at chill temperatures. Although absence is preferred, a count of less than 20 CFU/gramme is considered satisfactory and 100 CFU/g or more unsatisfactory/potentially hazardous.

9.3.2.1.2 *Clostridium perfringens* and *Staphylococcus aureus*

A count of <20 CFU/g of *Clostridium perfringens* or *Staphylococcus aureus* is considered satisfactory, 20 to up to 100/g acceptable, 100 to 10,000 (10^4/g) unsatisfactory and above 10^4/g unacceptable/potentially hazardous.

9.3.2.1.3 Pathogenic *Bacillus* spp

A count of up to 1,000 CFU/g (10^3/g) of *Bacillus cereus* and other pathogenic *Bacillus* species is considered satisfactory, 10^3 – 10^4/g acceptable, 10^4 – 10^5/g unsatisfactory and 10^5/g or more unacceptable/potentially hazardous.

Note: *Bacillus thuringiensis* is a biological control used widely on produce. However, it is indistinguishable from

B. cereus by conventional microbiological testing. Therefore, if a high level of *B. cereus* is found, investigate whether this biological control has been used.

9.3.2.2 Aerobic Colony Count (ACC)

No microbiological guidelines have been set by PHLS for ACC in fresh fruit and vegetables. However, In the case of prepared mixed salads and crudités, Satisfactory has been defined as being $< 10^6$ cfu/g (1,000,000 per gramme of sample), acceptable as being between 10^6 and 10^7 cfu/g, and unsatisfactory at greater than 10^7 cfu/g .

When an unsatisfactory ACC is encountered, the microorganisms that predominate could be identified in order to provide a more helpful interpretation.

9.3.2.3 Enterobacteriaceae

Criteria for these organisms are not appropriate for fresh fruit and vegetables or to sandwiches and other ready to eat items containing salad vegetables. This is because fresh fruit and vegetables generally carry high levels of Enterobacteriaceae, many of which will be harmless and naturally present. Testing should therefore be carried out specifically for those organisms of concern. However, Enterobacteriaceae (or Coliforms) can be used as indicators to determine the microbiological effect of a process e.g. sampling before and after harvesting.

9.3.2.4 *E. coli* (Total) and *Listeria* species (spp) (Total)

The presence of such organisms is generally taken as being indicators for the potential presence of pathogenic strains.

The detection of these organisms in produce requires investigation, risk assessment and management and close monitoring of trends, taking into consideration the PHLS guidelines for RTE products. It is good practice to notify the customer of any positive results. Levels of greater than 100cfu per gramme must be notified to the customer.

For irrigation water *E. coli* is often used as the indicator organism for faecal contamination. When *E. coli* is regularly detected, a risk assessment should take place and this water should, where practicable, be applied to lower risk crops (Table 7). Where this is not practicable, the risk of contamination of produce should be assessed.

9.4   Interpretation of Results

All results should be used as an indicator of the general microflora of the produce.

Trend data should be generated and used together with risk assessment in the interpretation of results. Rolling averages can be on a weekly, monthly or quarterly basis, as most appropriate, and assigned warning levels can be associated with each rolling average as stated above. Rising trends may be attributed to conditions prevalent, handling at harvest and postharvest, and storage conditions (e.g. temperature), however these must be investigated.

9.5   Useful Information Sources

Catalogue of Rapid Microbiological Methods
CCFRA Review No. 1 – 4th Edition (2000)

'Development and Use of Microbiological Criteria for Foods'
Institute of Food Science & Technology, 2nd Edition, 1999. www.ifst.org.uk

'Guidelines for the microbiological quality of some ready-to-eat foods sampled at the point of sale'
PHLS, Communicable Disease and Public Health, Vol 3, No. 3, pp 163–7, September 2000. www.phls.org.uk

'Microbiological quality of retail imported unprepared whole lettuces: A PHLS Food Working Group study'
J Fd Prot, Vol 62, No. 4, 1999, pp 325–8.

'Survey of microbial and chemical quality of fresh lettuce and spinach'
Scottish Food Co-ordinating Committee, June 1998

'An Introduction to the Practice of Microbiological Risk Assessment for Food Industry Applications'
CCFRA Guideline No. 28 (2000)

'The Control of Microbial Hazards – A produce industry guide'
Fresh Produce Consortium, 1998.

'Fresh, Nutritious and Safe – A guide to the production of safe food'
Fresh Produce Consortium

Food Safety Guidelines for the Fresh-cut Produce Industry
Third Edition, International Fresh Cut Produce Association

'Canadian Food Inspection Agency – Food of Plant Origin Division – Fresh Fruits and Vegetables – Code of Practice for Minimally Processed Ready-to-Eat Vegetables'
www.cfia-acia.agr.ca/english/plaveg/fresh/read-eat_e.shtml
Canadian Food Inspection Agency, Food of Plant Origin Division

'Surface decontamination of fruits and vegetables eaten raw: a Review'
Dr Larry R. Beuchat, WHO/FSF/FOS/98.2, World Health Organization Food Safety Unit, Geneva, 1998

'Microbiological safety evaluations and recommendations on fresh produce'
C. De Roever, National Advisory Committee on Microbiological Criteria for Foods
Food Control, 1999, 10, pp117 – 143

'Guidelines for drinking water quality – microbiological aspects'
WHO, 2000, www.who.int/water_sanitation_health/Documents/GDWQtraining/S03.pdf

10.   Incident Management

In the case of a food safety issue arising, timely action must be taken to protect consumer safety. Actions include:

1.   Immediate liaison with customers (food manufacturers and/or retailers).

2.   Seek specialist advice to enable a risk assessment of the hazard found to be carried out.

3.   If it is assessed that there is a significant risk of there being a health hazard in the final product, the food manufacturer and/or retailer to liaise with customers on recall of final product and/or inform regulatory authorities.

      If any form of public recall is involved, the extent of the problem must be made clear. For example:

      • Restricted to a particular batch/size/distribution area;
      • Reassure that all other batches/sizes/products are safe;
      • Number of packages involved;
      • Speed and efficiency of recall; and
      • Cause of fault being investigated

4.   Full traceability will enable all potentially affected products to be identified and the incident managed effectively.

      Remedial actions in the supply chain should involve the consideration of:-

      i)   What to do to re-establish control and prevent reoccurrence of the hazard
      ii)   What to do with product and raw material held in stock or in the supply chain that might be out of specification
      iii)   When the action taken should be completed, i.e. the timescale for the action
      iv)   Who has responsibility for the action

11.   Useful Contacts

It is recommended that each company maintains an up to date crisis contact list to include the following key organisations:-

ADAS
Gleadthorpe Research Centre
Meden Vale
Mansfield
NG20 9PF
www.adas.co.uk
Tel: +44 (0) 1623 844331
Fax: +44 (0) 1623 847424

ADAS
Microbiology Laboratory
Woodthorne
Wergs Road
Wolverhampton
WV6 8TQ
www.adas.co.uk
Tel: +44 (0) 1902 693277
Fax: +44 (0) 1902 693310

Campden & Chorleywood Food RA (CCFRA)
Chipping Campden
GL55 6LD
www.campden.co.uk
T: +44 (0) 1386 842000
F: +44 (0) 1486 842100

Chilled Food Association (CFA)
P O Box 14811
London
NW10 9ZR
www.chilledfood.org
T: +44 (0) 20 8451 0503
F: +44 (0) 20 8459 8061

Fresh Produce Consortium (FPC)
Minerva Business Park
Lynch Wood
Peterborough
PE2 6FT
www.freshproduce.org.uk
T: +44 (0) 1733 239117
F: +44 (0) 1733 237118

National Farmers Union (NFU)
Agriculture House
164 Shaftesbury Avenue
London
WC2H 8HL
www.nfu.org.uk
T: +44 (0) 20 7331 7200
F: +44 (0) 20 7331 7313

SWABBING & SAMPLING – KEY POINTS

Swabbing

- Use swabs appropriate to the size of the surface being tested, sterile sponges can also be used for larger areas.
- Use an appropriate carrier gel for transportation to the laboratory
- If swabbing after cleaning ensure that a deactivation agent has been applied beforehand i.e. swabs must be pre treated with deactivating agent prior to swabbing. Deactivation agents are available from most laboratories.
- Swabs should be tested within 24 hours of swabbing.

Produce Sampling

- Where plastic sample bags are used they must be sterile and should be sufficiently robust not to tear
- The bag should be labelled and secured with a tamperproof seal
- The sample should be labelled to enable it to be traced
- Samples taken outside normal working hours should be delivered to a holding fridge where the temperature is monitored and maintained at 0–5°C
- If the sample is taken outside of office hours, it should be delivered to the laboratory in a cool box/mobile refrigerator pre-cooled to 0–5°C as soon as practicable the following day
- Samples must not be frozen before submission to a laboratory

Water Sampling

- Appropriate clean, new, sterile containers must be used
- A minimum of a 500 ml sample should be taken
- Samples should be taken to the laboratory with the minimum delay
- If there is a delay in testing the sample of more than 6 hours, it is good practice to maintain the sample at 0–5°C
- Results may be erroneous if samples are taken from the surface of the water, owing to UV effects
- Choose your sample point with care. Samples should be taken from the end of the water delivery system to best reflect water quality.
- When taking samples of chlorinated water, the chlorine must be neutralised with sodium thiosulphate.

NOTE:

Great care must be taken during sampling to ensure that samples are not contaminated by the procedure.

PRE-EMPLOYMENT MEDICAL SCREENING QUESTIONNAIRE

FULL NAME: _____

DATE OF BIRTH: _____

DATE OF ENGAGEMENT: _____

1. Have you now, or have you over the last seven days, suffered from diarrhoea and/or vomiting?   YES/NO

2. At present, are you suffering from:

    i)   Skin trouble affecting hands, arms or face?   YES/NO

    ii) Boils, styes or septic fingers?   YES/NO

    iii) Discharge from eye, ear or gums/mouth?   YES/NO

3. Do you suffer from:

    i)   Recurring skin or ear trouble?   YES/NO

    ii) A recurring bowel disorder?   YES/NO

4. Have you ever had, or are you now known to be a carrier of typhoid or paratyphoid?   YES/NO

5. In the last 21 days have you been in contact with anyone, at home or abroad, who may have been suffering from typhoid or paratyphoid?   YES/NO

6. Have you been abroad in the last three weeks?   YES/NO

7. If YES, were you ill?   YES/NO

IF ALL THE ANSWERS TO THE ABOVE QUESTIONS ARE 'NO', THE EMPLOYEE IS FIT TO BE EMPLOYED AS A FOOD HANDLER. IF YES HAS BEEN ANSWERED TO ANY OF THE ABOVE QUESTIONS, SEEK MEDICAL ADVICE BEFORE EMPLOYMENT.

SIGNATURE OF EMPLOYEE:-   _____

SIGNATURE OF EMPLOYER:-   _____

SIGNATURE OF MEDICAL PRACTITIONER (if applicable):_____

PRE-EMPLOYMENT HYGIENE TRAINING MATERIAL

Personal Responsibility

If you are employed as a food handler you are responsible for helping to ensure that food reaches consumers in a condition that doesn't harm them. You must remember that you are making food for people to eat, and their well-being and safety depends on you.

Good hygiene is necessary for your company, job security and is required by law.

Harm can mean food poisoning by bacteria and viruses (germs), poisoning by chemicals (e.g. cleaning materials), or physical damage from foreign bodies (e.g. glass).

Food Poisoning Bacteria and Viruses (Germs)

Germs are organisms that are so small you can't see them, but if not controlled can be found everywhere. Food poisoning bacteria and viruses can't be allowed in chilled ready to eat foods.

Important food poisoning organisms include:-

Salmonella
E. coli O157
Listeria monocytogenes
Staphylococcus aureus
Campylobacter
Clostridium perfringens
Bacillus cereus
Clostridium botulinum (botulism bacteria)
some viruses

These can be found in a variety of places including:-

- Animals (e.g. food animals, birds, pets, pests and food animals)
- Raw food (e.g. raw meat, poultry, vegetables)
- Raw milk
- Soil, dirt and dust
- Human beings – intestines, skin (e.g. hands, cuts), nose, mouth and hair
- Clothing and footwear
- Water, especially lying open in pools or puddles
- Air
- Surfaces (e.g. floors, walls, factory equipment, dirty cleaning
- Equipment, outer packaging, gloves)
- Waste (e.g. trimmings, reject materials)
- Toilet areas

Food poisoning usually causes a stomach upset – vomiting and diarrhoea, but it can sometimes be more serious than this, even causing death.

Chemicals

Chemicals in food factories are needed for cleaning, disinfecting and keeping machinery working properly. If chemicals are used wrongly (e.g. too much, in the wrong place, mixed with other chemicals, not washed off as instructed, or can taint the product) they can become poisonous, may harm yourself or the consumer.

Examples include:-

- Cleaning chemicals
- Disinfectants
- Lubricants
- Perfume

Foreign Bodies

Foreign bodies lead to dissatisfied customers who feel their well being has been affected. They may also cause harm e.g. glass.

Examples of foreign bodies include:-

- Glass and hard plastics
- Nuts, bolts and electrical wire
- Pieces of packaging material
- Bones or shells
- Wood
- Jewellery
- Cigarette ends
- Plasters
- Contact lenses and glasses
- Cleaning equipment (e.g. brush bristles, cloths)
- Hair
- Make up and nail varnish
- Flies and insects

WHAT YOU MUST DO TO AVOID THESE PROBLEMS

> **Always follow factory rules and instructions**
> **Prevent contamination**
> **Don't let bacteria, foreign bodies or chemicals get onto the food**

DO

- ✓ Always wear protective clothing provided
- ✓ Change protective clothing when instructed, following the factory procedures
- ✓ Wash hands thoroughly as instructed, especially after using the toilet, after handling waste, after handling raw materials and before touching ready to eat foods
- ✓ Report any septic boils and cuts to your immediate manager
- ✓ Cover cuts and blemishes with a blue waterproof plaster as blue is easily seen
- ✓ Report sickness and/or diarrhoea to your manager. This includes contact with other people who have had sickness or diarrhoea
- ✓ Store chemicals and cleaning equipment away in separate storage areas before handling foods
- ✓ Be careful in your use of water – it can spread germs. Only use it as instructed
- ✓ Ensure that equipment is always clean
- ✓ Stick to the Company's hygiene rules

DON'T

- ✗ Start work if suffering from vomiting or diarrhoea
- ✗ Start work before you have washed your hands
- ✗ Wear jewellery or watches, except as allowed by the Company
- ✗ Smoke except in special areas allowed by the Company
- ✗ Sneeze or cough over food – if you have to wipe or blow your nose use a disposable tissue and then wash your hands
- ✗ Scratch or touch skin or hair
- ✗ Bite your nails, or lick your fingers
- ✗ Spit
- ✗ Eat in the factory
- ✗ Allow anything that has been on the floor to be packed as food or come Into contact with food
- ✗ Use dirty containers or utensils
- ✗ Use hoses near open product and never spray floors or packaging with water

Prevent the growth of bacteria

Sometimes you don't even need germs to grow to cause food poisoning. Examples of these are *E coli* 0157, viruses, Campylobacter and even Salmonella. However, food poisoning is often caused when bacteria are allowed to grow to high numbers. To do this they need moisture, warmth and time. The growth of bacteria slows down a lot at less than about 8°C and more than about 50°C. If conditions are right, they can double their numbers as often as every 20 minutes. This means that one germ can grow

to nearly 17 million by the end of a shift. This is more than enough to cause food poisoning. It is particularly important to cover and move food to chilled store rooms quickly.

A low temperature, even freezing, will not kill germs but will slow their growth right down.

DO

- ✓ Keep things that are meant to be cold, cold (usually 5°C or less)
- ✓ Products that need to be chilled should be chilled as soon as possible
- ✓ Keep things that are meant to be hot, hot (usually 63°C or more)
- ✓ Keep things dry if instructed to do so
- ✓ Keep things clean
- ✓ Clean as you go
- ✓ Report faulty refrigeration or other equipment to your manager

DON'T

- ✗ Leave food at room temperature (in the danger zone (8–50°C), or outside the factory
- ✗ Take food out of the fridge before directed
- ✗ Leave fridge doors open
- ✗ Use water unnecessarily in 'dry areas'
- ✗ Neglect difficult to clean areas when cleaning – these may provide breeding ground for germs

Destroying Germs

Cooking is usually carried out to destroy germs. Always ensure that cooking instructions are followed.

DO

- ✓ Always heat or cook foods to the temperatures and times required
- ✓ If there seems to be a problem with cooking report it immediately to your supervisor

DON'T

- ✗ Ever allow inadequately heated foods to be packed

Q1   Why should food be stored in a fridge?
A1   To slow the growth of germs.

Q2   Why is special clean protective clothing worn?
A2   To protect food from contamination.

Q3   Why is it important to keep the factory clean?
A3   To prevent the spread of germs.

Q4   When should you wash your hands?
A4   Before you handle food.

Q5   Why should wounds and skin blemishes be covered?
A5   To prevent contamination of food from germs on/in them.

Q6   Why are blue coloured plasters used?
A6   They are easy to see if they fall off.

Q7   What are the key conditions needed for germs to grow?
A7   Warmth (must give this point), food, water.

Q8   How do you stop germs growing?
A8   Refrigeration (must give), heat, drying.

Q9   What is the main way we destroy germs?
A9   Heat.

Q10   What must you do if you drop food on the floor?
A10   Ensure it is not used.

Q11   Why must cooked foods be protected from contact with raw materials?
A11   To prevent contamination

Q12   What must you do if equipment is faulty?
A12   Report it to your manager.

Q13   What must you do if you have vomiting or diarrhoea?
A13   Preferably, stay at home, but at least report it to your manager before starting work.

Q14   Name two common symptoms of food poisoning
A14   Diarrhoea, vomiting.

Q15   List three types of foreign bodies or chemical contamination
A15   See training material.

OPERATIVES ONLY

SELECTION QUESTIONNAIRE – FOOD HYGIENE AWARENESS

Name...

Date...

Questions. Please give your answers in the space provided.

Q1.	Why should food be stored in a fridge?	
Q2.	Why is special clean protective clothing worn?	
Q3.	Why is it important to keep the factory clean?	
Q4.	When should you wash your hands?	
Q5.	Why should wounds and skin blemishes be covered?	
Q6.	Why are blue coloured plasters used?	
Q7.	What are the key conditions needed for germs to grow?	
Q8.	How do you stop germs growing?	
Q9.	What is the main way we destroy germs?	
Q10.	What must you do if you drop food on the floor?	
Q11.	Why must cooked foods be protected from contact with raw materials?	
Q12.	What must you do if equipment is faulty?	
Q13.	What must you do if you have vomiting or diarrhoea?	
Q14.	Name two common symptoms of food poisoning	
Q15.	List three types of foreign bodies or chemical contamination	

GUIDANCE WORKING GROUP MEMBERSHIP

Mrs Sue Feuerhelm	Fisher Foods
Mr Ed Havis	Fisher Foods
Mr David Kennedy	Geest
Dr Chris Foulds	G's Marketing
Dr Malcolm Knight	Heinz Frozen & Chilled Foods
Dr Sheila Benson	Uniq

Miss Kaarin Goodburn Chilled Food Association Ltd
P O Box 14811
London NW10 9ZR
www.chilledfood.org
cfa@chilledfood.org

With comments received from:

ADAS
National Farmers Union